BOB DYLAN
ANTHOLOGY 2

AMSCO PUBLICATIONS
NEW YORK/LONDON/SYDNEY

Order No. AM 934384
US International Standard Book Number: 0.8256.1530.5
UK International Standard Book Number: 0.7119.5407.0

Exclusive Distributors:
Music Sales Corporation
257 Park Avenue South, New York, NY 10010 USA
Music Sales Limited
8/9 Frith Street, London W1V 5TZ England
Music Sales Pty. Limited
120 Rothschild Avenue, Rosebery, Sydney, NSW 2018 Australia

Printed in the United States of America by
Vicks Lithograph and Printing Corporation

CONTENTS

Absolutely Sweet Marie 4

Boots Of Spanish Leather 10

Changing Of The Guards 16

Chimes Of Freedom 12

Dear Landlord 21

Desolation Row 24

Dignity 32

Don't Think Twice, It's Alright 38

Foot Of Pride 42

Girl Of The North Country 50

A Hard Rain's A-Gonna Fall 52

Heart Of Mine 27

Highway 61 Revisited 47

I Believe In You 55

It Ain't Me, Babe 71

It's All Over Now, Baby Blue 62

It's Alright, Ma (I'm Only Bleeding) 64

John Brown 68

Just Like Tom Thumb's Blues 74

Lay Down Your Weary Tune 76

Leopard-Skin Pill-Box Hat 78

Like A Rolling Stone 84

Love Minus Zero/No Limit 88

Maggie's Farm 81

Masters Of War 90

Most Likely You Go Your Way And I'll Go Mine 92

Mr. Tambourine Man 96

My Back Pages 99

New Morning 102

One More Cup Of Coffee (Valley Below) 107

Political World 110

Positively Fourth Street 118

Ring Them Bells 120

Seven Days 127

She Belongs To Me 136

Shooting Star 138

Subterranean Homesick Blues 149

The Times They Are A-Changin' 152

This Wheel's On Fire 157

Tombstone Blues 160

Tonight I'll Be Staying Here With You 144

Too Much Of Nothing 164

Unbelievable 184

Up To Me 154

Visions Of Johanna 194

Watching The River Flow 170

When The Night Comes Falling From The Sky 176

When The Ship Comes In 182

Wiggle Wiggle 166

You're A Big Girl Now 192

Absolutely Sweet Marie

Words and Music by Bob Dylan

Moderately, with a beat

Boots Of Spanish Leather

Words and Music by Bob Dylan

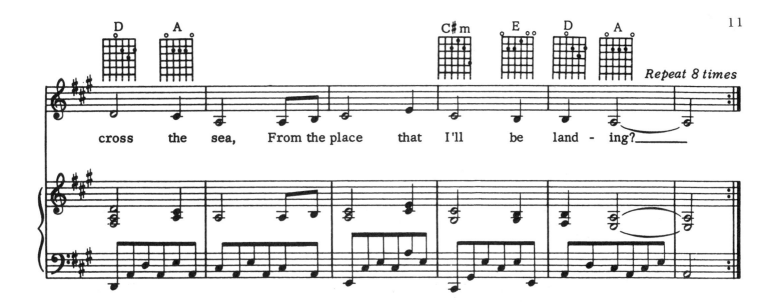

cross   the   sea,   From the place   that   I'll   be   land - ing?_____

2. No there's nothin' you can send me my own true love,
   There's nothin' I wish to be ownin',
   Just carry yourself back to me unspoiled,
   From across that lonesome ocean.

3. Oh, but I just thought you might long want something fine
   Made of silver or of golden,
   Either from the mountains of Madrid
   Or from the coast of Barcelona.

4. Oh but if I had the stars from the darkest night
   And the diamonds from the deepest ocean,
   I'd forsake them all for your sweet kiss
   For that's all I'm wishin' to be ownin'.

5. That I might be gone a long ole time
   And it's only that I'm askin',
   Is there somethin' I can send you to remember me by
   To make your time more easy passin'.

6. Oh how can, how can you ask me again,
   It only brings me sorrow,
   The same thing I want from you today
   I would want again tomorrow.

7. I got a letter on a lonesome day,
   It was from her ship a-sailin'
   Saying I don't know when I'll be comin' back again,
   It depends on how I'm a-feelin'.

8. Well, if you my love must think that-a-way,
   I'm sure your mind is roamin',
   I'm sure your heart is not with me,
   But with the country to where you're goin'.

9. So take heed, take heed of the western wind,
   Take heed of the stormy weather,
   And yes, there's something you can send back to me,
   Spanish boots of Spanish leather.

Chimes Of Freedom

Words and Music by Bob Dylan

2.   In the city's melted furnace, unexpectedly we watched
     With faces hidden while the walls were tightening,
     As the echo of the wedding bells before the blowin' rain
     Dissolved into the bells of the lightning.
     Tolling for the rebel, tolling for the rake,
     Tolling for the luckless, the abandoned an' forsaked,
     Tolling for the outcast, burnin' constantly at stake
     An' we gazed upon the chimes of freedom flashing.

3.   Thru the mad mystic hammering of the wild ripping hail
     The sky cracked its poems in naked wonder
     That the clinging of the church bells blew far into the breeze
     Leaving only bells of lightning and its thunder
     Striking for the gentle, striking for the kind,
     Striking for the guardians and protectors of the mind
     An' the unpawned painter behind beyond his rightful time
     An' we gazed upon the chimes of freedom flashing.

4.   Thru the wild cathedral evening the rain unraveled tales
     For the disrobed faceless forms of no position
     Tolling for the tongues with no place to bring their thoughts
     All down in taken for granted situations
     Tolling for the deaf an' blind, tolling for the mute,
     Tolling for the mistreated, mateless mother, the mistitled prostitute
     For the misdemeanor outlaw chased an' cheated by pursuit
     An' we gazed upon the chimes of freedom flashing.

5.   Even tho a cloud's white curtain in a far off corner flashed
     An' the hypnotic splattered mist was slowly lifting
     Electric light still struck like arrows fired but for the ones
     Condemned to drift or else be kept from drifting
     Tolling for the searching ones, on their speechless seeking trail
     For the lonesome hearted lovers, with too personal a tale
     An' for each unharmful gentle soul misplaced inside a jail
     An' we gazed upon the chimes of freedom flashing.

6.   Starry eyed an' laughing as I recall when we were caught
     Trapped by no track of hours for they hanged suspended
     As we listened one last time an' we watched with one last look
     Spellbound an' swallowed till the tolling ended
     Tolling for the aching ones whose wounds cannot be nursed
     For the countless confused, accused, misused, stung out ones an' worse
     An' for every hung up person in the whole wide universe
     An' we gazed upon the chimes of freedom flashing.

Changing Of The Guards

Words and Music by Bob Dylan

18

3. The cold-blooded moon;
   The captain waits above the celebration,
   Sending his thoughts to a beloved maid
   Whose ebony face is beyond communication.
   The captain is down but still believing that his love will be repaid.

4. They shaved her head.
   She was torn between Jupiter and Apollo.
   A messenger arrived with a black nightingale.
   I seen her on the stairs and I couldn't help but follow,
   Follow her down past the fountain where they lifted her veil.

5. I stumbled to my feet,
   I rode past destruction in the ditches
   With the stitches still mending 'neath a heart-shaped tattoo.
   Renegade priests and treacherous young witches
   Were handing out the flowers that I'd given to you.

6. The palace of mirrors
   Where dog soldiers are reflected;
   The endless road and the wailing of chimes;
   The empty rooms where her memory is protected,
   Where the angels' voices whisper to the souls of previous times.

7. She wakes him up
   Forty-eight hours later; the sun is breaking
   Near broken chains, mountain laurel and rolling rocks.
   She's begging to know what measures he now will be taking.
   He's pulling her down and she's clutching onto his long golden locks.

8. "Gentlemen," he said,
   "I don't need your organization. I've shined your shoes,
   I've moved your mountains and marked your cards.
   But Eden is burning. Either brace yourself for elimination,
   Or else your hearts must have the courage for the changing of the guards."

9. Peace will come
   With tranquility and splendor on the wheels of fire,
   But will bring us no reward than her false idols fall,
   And cruel death surrenders with its pale ghost retreating
   Between the King and the Queen of Swords.

10. *Instrumental*

Dear Landlord

WORDS AND MUSIC BY BOB DYLAN

Moderately slow

Additional lyrics

2. Dear landlord,
   Please heed these words that I speak,
   I know you've suffered much,
   But in this you are not so unique.
   All of us at times we might work too hard
   To have it too fast and too much,
   And anyone can fill his life up with things he can see,
   But he just cannot touch.

3. Dear landlord,
   Please don't dismiss my case,
   I'm not about to argue
   I'm not about to move to no other place.
   Now each of us has his own special gift,
   And you know this was meant to be true,
   And if you don't underestimate me,
   I won't underestimate you.

Desolation Row

WORDS AND MUSIC BY BOB DYLAN

Slowly with a steady beat

They're sell-ing post-cards of the hang-ing _____ They're paint-ing the pass-ports

brown _____ The beau-ty par-lor's filled with sail-ors _____ The cir-cus is in town _____

Additional lyrics

2. Cinderella, she seems so easy
"It takes one to know one," she smiles
And then puts her hands in her back pocket
Bette Davis style
And in comes Romeo, he's moaning
"You belong to Me I Believe"
And someone says, "You're in the wrong place, my friend
You'd better leave"
And the only sound that's left
After the ambulances go
Is Cinderella sweeping up
On Desolation Row

3. Now the moon is almost hidden
The stars are beginning to hide
The fortune telling lady
Has even taken all her things inside
All except for Cain and Abel
And the hunchback of Notre Dame
Everybody is making love
Or else expecting rain
And the Good Samaritan, he's dressing
He's getting ready for the show
He's going to the carnival tonight
On Desolation Row

4. Now Ophelia, she's 'neath the window
For her I feel so afraid
On her twenty-second birthday
She already is an old maid
To her, death is quite romantic
She wears an iron vest
Her profession's her religion
Her sin is her lifelessness
And though her eyes are fixed upon
Noah's great rainbow
She spends her time peeking
Into Desolation Row

5. Einstein, disguised as Robin Hood
With his memories in a trunk
Passed this way an hour ago
With his friend, a jealous monk
He looked so immaculately frightful
As he bummed a cigarette
Then he went off sniffing drain pipes
And reciting the alphabet
Now you would not think to look at him
But he was famous long ago
For playing the electric violin
On Desolation Row

6. Doctor Filth, he keeps his world
Inside of a leather cup
But all his sexless patient
They're trying to blow it up
Now his nurse, some local loser
She's in charge of the cyanide hole
And she also keeps the cards that read
"Have Mercy on His Soul"
They all play on penny whistles
You can hear them blow
If you lean your head out far enough
From Desolation Row

7. Across the street they've nailed the curtains
They're getting ready for the feast
The Phantom of the Opera
A perfect image of a priest
They're spoon feeding Casanova
To get him to feel more assured
Then they'll kill him with self-confidence
After poisoning him with words
And the Phantom's shouting to skinny girls
"Get Outta Here If You Don't Know
Casanova is just being punished for going
To Desolation Row"

8. Now at midnight all the agents
And the super human crew
Come out and round up everyone
That know more than they do
Then they bring them to the factory
Where the heart-attack machine
Is strapped across their shoulders
And then the kerosene
Is brought down from the castles
By insurance men who go
Check to see that nobody is escaping
To Desolation Row

9. Praise be to Nero's Neptune
The Titanic sails at dawn
And everybody's shouting
"Which Side Are You On?"
And Ezra Pound and T.S. Eliot
Fighting in the captain's tower
While calypso singers laugh at them
And fishermen hold flowers
Between the windows of the sea
Where lovely mermaids flow
and nobody has to think too much
About Desolation Row

10. Yes, I received your letter yesterday
(About the time the door knob broke)
When you asked how I was doing
Was that some kind of joke?
All these people that you mentioned
Yes, I know them, they're quite lame
I had to rearrange their faces
And give them all another name
Right now I can't read too good
Don't send me no more letters no
Not unless you mail them
From Desolation Row.

Heart Of Mine

Words and Music by Bob Dylan

DIGNITY

WORDS AND MUSIC BY BOB DYLAN

Moderate shuffle beat

1. Fat man look-in' in a ___ blade of steel, ___
2.-4. *See additional lyrics*

Thin man look-in' at his last meal.

34

Additional lyrics

2. Blind man breakin' out of a trance,
   Puts both his hands in the pockets of chance.
   Hopin' to find one circumstance
   Of dignity.

   I went to the wedding of Mary-Lou,
   She said, "I don't want nobody see me talkin' to you."
   Said she could get killed if she told me what she knew
   About dignity.

      I went down where the vultures feed,
      I would've gone deeper, but there wasn't any need.
      Heard the tongues of angels and the tongues of men
      Wasn't any difference to me.

   Chilly wind sharp as a razor blade,
   House on fire, debts unpaid.
   Gonna stand at the window, gonna ask the maid
   Have you seen dignity.

3. Drinkin' man listens to the voice he hears
   In a crowed room full of covered up mirrors.
   Lookin' into the lost forgotten years
   For dignity.

   Met Prince Phillip at the home of the blues
   Said he'd give me information if his name wasn't used.
   He wanted money up front, said he was abused
   By dignity.

      Footprints runnin' cross the silver sand,
      Steps goin' down into tattoo land.
      I met the sons of darkness and the sons of light
      In the bordertowns of despair.

   Got no place to fade, got no coat,
   I'm on the rollin' river in a jerkin' boat.
   Tryin' to read a note somebody wrote
   About dignity.

4. Sick man lookin' for the doctor's cure,
   Lookin' at his hands for the lines that were,
   And into every masterpiece of literature
   For dignity.

   Englishmen stranded in the blackheart wind
   Combin' his hair back, his future looks thin.
   Bites the bullet and he looks within
   For dignity.

      Someone showed me a picture and I just laughed,
      Dignity never been photographed.
      I went into the red, went into the black,
      Into the valley of dry bone dreams.

   So many roads, so much at stake,
   So many dead ends, I'm at the edge of the lake.
   Sometimes I wonder what it's going to take
   To find dignity.

Don't Think Twice, It's All Right

Words and Music by Bob Dylan

FOOT OF PRIDE
WORDS AND MUSIC BY BOB DYLAN

Moderate beat, quasi recitative

1. Like the li - on tears the flesh _ off of a man, ____ So
can a wom-an who pass-es her-self off __ as a male. _ They sang
"Dan-ny Boy" at his fu - n'ral, and the Lord's _ Prayer.

Additional lyrics

2. Hear ya got a brother named James, don't forget faces or names.
   Sunken cheeks and his blood is mixed,
   He looked straight into the sun and said, "revenge is mine."
   But he drinks, and drinks can be fixed.
   Sing me one more song, about ya love me to the moon and the stranger,
   And your fall by the sword love affair with Eroll Flynn.
   In these times of compassion when conformity's in fashion,
   Say one more stupid thing to me before the final nail is driven in.

   (Chorus)

3. There's a retired businessman named Red, cast down from heaven and he's out of his head.
   He feeds off of everyone that he can touch,
   He said he only deals in cash or sells tickets to a plane crash.
   He's not somebody that you play around with much.
   Miss Delilah is his, a philistine is what she is.
   She'll do wondrous works with your fate,
   Feed you coconut bread, spice buns in your bed,
   If you don't mind sleepin' with your head face down in a grave.

   (Chorus)

4. Well, they'll choose a man for you to meet tonight.
   You'll play the fool and learn how to walk through doors,
   How to enter into the gates of paradise.
   No, how to carry a burden too heavy to be yours.
   Yeah, from the stage they'll be tryin' to get water outta rocks.
   A whore will pass the hat, collect a hundred grand and say, "thanks."
   They like to take all this money from sin, build big universities to study in,
   Sing "Amazing Grace" all the way to the Swiss banks.

   (Chorus)

5. They got some beautiful people out there, man.
   They can be a terror to your mind and show you how to hold your tongue.
   They got mystery written all over their forehead.
   They kill babies in the crib and say only the good die young.
   They don't believe in mercy.
   Judgment on them is something that you'll never see.
   They can exalt you up or bring you down main route,
   Turn you into anything that they want you to be.

   (Chorus)

6. Yes, I guess I loved him too,
   I can still see him in my mind climbin' that hill.
   Did he make it to the top? Well, he probably did and dropped,
   Struck down by the strength of the will.
   Ain't nothin' left here, partner, just the dust of a plague that has left this whole town afraid.
   From now on, this'll be where you're from.
   Let the dead bury the dead. Your time will come.
   Let hot iron blow as he raised the shade.

   (Chorus to instrumental fade)

HIGHWAY 61 REVISITED

Words and Music by Bob Dylan

48

2. Well Georgia Sam he had a bloody nose
   Welfare Department they wouldn't give him no clothes
   He asked poor Howard where can I go
   Howard said there's only one place I know
   Sam said tell me quick man I got to run
   Ol' Howard just pointed with his gun
   And said that way down on Highway 61.

3. Well Mack the Finger said to Louie the King
   I got forty red white and blue shoe strings
   And a thousand telephones that don't ring
   Do you know where I can get rid of these things
   And Louie the King said let me think for a minute son
   And he said yes I think it can be easily done
   Just take everything down to Highway 61.

4. Now the fifth daughter on the twelfth night
   Told the first father that things weren't right
   My complexion she said is much too white
   He said come here and step into the light he says hmm you're right
   Let me tell the second mother this has been done
   But the second mother was with the seventh son
   And they were both out on Highway 61.

5. Now the rovin' gambler he was very bored
   He was tryin' to create a next world war
   He found a promoter who nearly fell off the floor
   He said I never engaged in this kind of thing before
   But yes I think it can be very easily done
   We'll just put some bleachers out in the sun
   And have it on Highway 61.

GIRL OF THE NORTH COUNTRY

WORDS AND MUSIC BY BOB DYLAN

Additional Lyrics

2. Well if you go in the snowflake storm
   When the rivers freeze and summer ends,
   Please see she has a coat so warm
   To keep her from the howlin' winds.

3. Please see for me if her hair hangs long,
   If it rolls and flows all down her breast,
   Please see for me if her hair hangs long,
   That's the way I remember her best.

4. I'm a-wonderin' if she remembers me at all,
   Many times I've often prayed
   In the darkness of my night,
   In the brightness of my day,

5. So if you're trav'lin' in the north country fair,
   Where the winds hit heavy on the borderline,
   Remember me to one who lives there,
   She once was a true love of mine.

A Hard Rain's A-Gonna Fall

Words and Music by Bob Dylan

Moderato

A   Oh, what did you see, my blue eyed son?
      Oh, what did you see, my darling young one?

B   I saw a new born baby with wild wolves all around it,
      I saw a highway of diamonds with nobody on it,
      I saw a black branch with blood that kept drippin',
      I saw a room full of men with their hammers a-bleedin',
      I saw a white ladder all covered with water
      I saw ten thousand talkers whose tongues were all broken,

C   I saw guns and sharp swords in the hands of young children,
      And it's a hard, and it's a hard, it's a hard, it's a hard,
      And it's a hard rain's a gonna fall.

A   And what did you hear, my blue eyed son?
      And what did you hear, my darling young one?

B   I heard the sound of a thunder, it roared out a warnin',
      Heard the roar of a wave that could drown the whole world,
      Heard one hundred drummers whose hands were a blazin',
      Heard ten thousand whisperin' and nobody listenin',
      Heard one person starve, I heard many people laughin',
      Heard the song of a poet who died in the gutter,

C   Heard the sound of a clown who cried in the alley,
      And it's a hard, and it's a hard, it's a hard, it's a hard
      And it's a hard rain's a gonna fall.

A   Oh, who did you meet, my blue eyed son?
      Who did you meet, my darling young one?

B   I met a young child beside a dead pony,
      I met a white man who walked a black dog,
      I met a woman whose body was burning,
      I met a young girl, she gave me a rainbow,
      I met one man who was wounded in love,

C   I met another man who was wounded with hatred,
      And it's a hard, it's a hard, it's a hard, it's a hard
      It's a hard rain's a gonna fall.

A   Oh, what'll you do now, my blue eyed son?
      Oh, what'll you do now, my darling young one?

B   I'm a goin' back out 'fore the rain starts a fallin'.
      I'll walk to the depth of the deepest black forest,
      Where the people are many and their hands are all empty,
      Where the pellets of poison are flooding their waters,
      Where the home in the valley meets the damp dirty prison,
      Where the executioner's face is always well hidden,
      Where hunger is ugly, where souls are forgotten,
      Where black is the color, where none is the number,
      And I'll tell it and think it and speak it and breathe it,
      And reflect it from the mountain so all souls can see it,
      Then I'll stand on the ocean until I start sinkin',

C   But I'll know my song well before I start singin',
      And it's a hard, it's a hard, it's a hard, it's a hard,
      It's a hard rain's a gonna fall.

I Believe In You
Words and Music by Bob Dylan

Moderately slow

They ask me how I feel and if my love is real and how I'll know I'll make it through. And they, they look at me and

61

It's All Over Now, Baby Blue
Words and Music by Bob Dylan

Medium slow

You must leave now Take what you need, you think will last _____ But what-

ev- er you wish to keep, You bet-ter grab it fast. _____

Yon- der stands your or - phan, with his gun _____

63

2. The highway is for gamblers, better use your sins
Take what you have gathered from coincidence
The empty handed painter from your streets
Is drawing crazy patterns on your sheets
This sky too, is folding under you
And it's all over now, baby blue.

3. All your seasick sailors, they are rowing home
All your reindeer armies, are all going home
The lover who just walked out your door
Has taken all his blankets from the floor
The carpet too, is moving under you
And it's all over now, baby blue.

4. Leave your stepping stones behind, something calls for you
Forget the dead you've left, they will not follow you
The vagabond who's rapping at your door
Is standing in the clothes that you once wore
Strike another match, go start anew
And it's all over now, baby blue.

It's Alright, Ma (I'm Only Bleeding)

Words and Music by Bob Dylan

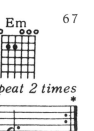

2. As some warn victory, some downfall
   Private reasons great or small
   Can be seen in the eyes of those that call
   To make all that should be killed, to crawl
   While others say, don't hate nothin' at all
   Except hatred

   Disillusioned words like bullets bark
   As human Gods aim for their mark
   Made everything from toy guns that spark
   To flesh colored Christs that glow in the dark
   It's easy to see without lookin' too far
   That not much,
   Is really sacred

   While preachers preach of evil fates
   Teachers teach that knowledge waits
   Can lead to hundred dollar plates
   Goodness hides behind its gates
   But even the president of the United States
   Sometimes must have
   To stand naked
   And though the rules of the road, have been lodged
   It's only peoples games that you got to dodge
   And it's alright ma, I can make it.

3. Advertising signs that con you
   Into thinking you're the one
   That can do what's never been done
   That can win, what's never been won
   Meantime life outside goes on
   All around you

   You lose yourself, you reappear
   You suddenly find you got nothin' to fear
   Alone you stand, with nobody near
   When a trembling distant voice unclear
   Startles your sleeping ears to hear
   That somebody thinks
   They really found you

   A question in your nerves is lit
   Yet you know there is no answer fit to satisfy.
   Insure you not to quit
   To keep it in your mind and not fergit
   That it is not he or she or them or it
   That you belong to
   Although the masters make the rules
   Of the wise men and the fools
   I got nothing, ma
   To live up to.

*4. For them that must obey authority
   That they do not respect in any degree
   Who despise their jobs, their destinies
   Speak jealously of them that are free
   Cultivate their flowers to be
   Nothing more than something
   They invest in

   While some unprinciples baptized
   To strict party platform ties
   Social clubs in drag disguise
   Outsiders achin' freely criticize
   Tell nothin' except who to idolize
   And say God bless him

   While one who sings with his tongue on fire
   Gargles in the rat race choir
   Bent out of shape from society's pliers
   Cares not to come up any higher
   But rather get you down in the hole
   That he's in
   But I mean no harm, nor put fault
   On anyone that lives in a vault
   But it's alright ma, if I can please him

*5. Old lady judges watch people in pairs
   Limited in sex, they dare
   To push fake moral insult, and stare
   While money doesn't talk, it swears
   Obscenity, who really cares
   Propaganda, all is phony

   While them that defend what they cannot see
   With a killer's pride, security
   It blows the minds most bitterly
   For them that think death's honesty
   Won't fall upon them naturally
   Life sometimes
   Must get lonely

   My eyes collide head on with stuffed graveyards,
   False Gods, I scuff
   At pettiness which plays so rough
   Walk upside down inside handcuffs
   Kick my legs to crash it off
   Say okay, I've had enough
   What else can you show me
   And if my thought dreams could be seen
   They'd probably put my head in a guillotine
   But it's alright ma
   It's life, and life only.

John Brown
Words and Music by Bob Dylan

Moderate rock

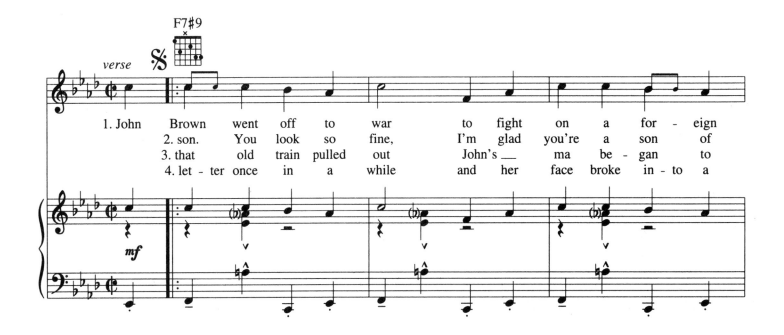

1. John Brown went off to war to fight on a for - eign
2. son. You look so fine, I'm glad you're a son of
3. that old train pulled out John's __ ma be - gan to
4. let - ter once in a while and her face broke in - to a

shore. His ma - ma sure was proud of him!
mine, you make me proud to know you hold a gun.
shout, tell - in' ev - 'ry - one in the neigh - bor - hood:
smile as she showed them to the peo - ple from next door.

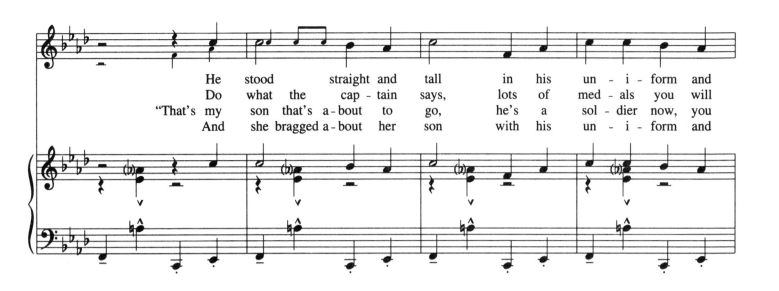

He stood straight and tall in his un - i - form and
Do what the cap - tain says, lots of med - als you will
"That's my son that's a - bout to go, he's a sol - dier now, you
And she bragged a - bout her son with his un - i - form and

to Coda
for final ending

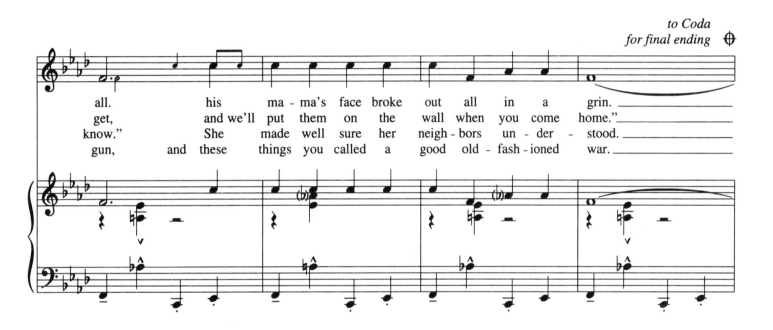

all. his ma - ma's face broke out all in a grin. _____
get, and we'll put them on the wall when you come home." _____
know." She made well sure her neigh - bors un - der - stood. _____
gun, and these things you called a good old - fash - ioned war. _____

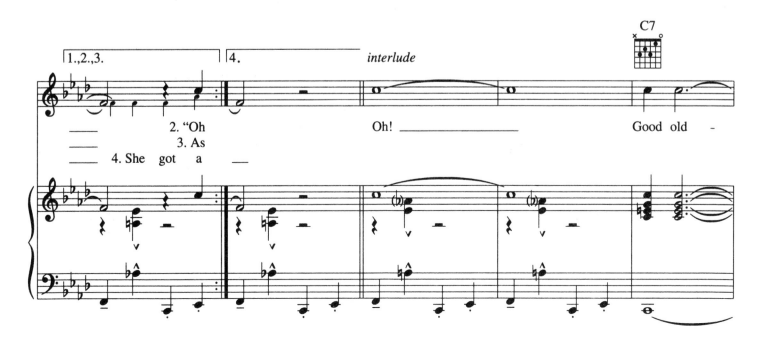

1.,2.,3.   4.   *interlude*

C7

____ 2. "Oh   Oh! _____   Good old -
____ 3. As
____ 4. She got a ____

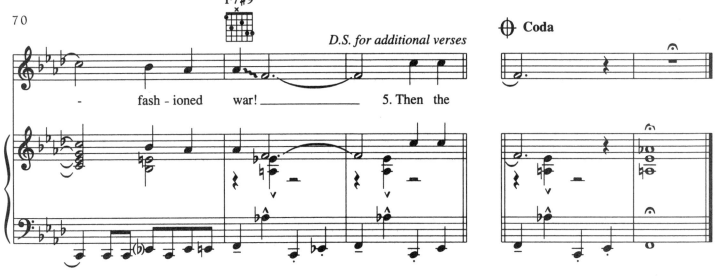

70

fash - ioned   war! _____   5. Then the

Additional lyrics

5. Then the letters ceased to come, for a long time they did not come.
   They ceased to come for about ten months or more.
   Then a letter finally came saying, "Go down and meet the train.
   Your son's a-coming home from the war."

6. She smiled and went right down, she looked everywhere around
   But she could not see her soldier son in sight.
   But as all the people passed, she saw her son at last
   When she did she could hardly believe her eyes.

7. Oh, his face was all shot up and his hand was all blown off
   And he wore a metal brace around his waist.
   He whispered kind of slow in a voice she did not know,
   While she couldn't even recognize his face!

   interlude
   Oh! Lord! Not even recognize his face.

8. "Oh, tell me, my darling son, pray tell me what they done.
   How is it you come to be this way?"
   He tried his best to talk, but his mouth could hardly move
   And the mother had to turn her face away.

9. "Don't you remember, Ma, when I went off to war
   You thought it was the best thing I could do?
   I was on the battle ground, you were home...acting proud.
   You wasn't there standing in my shoes."

10. "Oh, and I thought when I was there, God, what am I doing here?
    I'm a-tryin' to kill somebody or die tryin'.
    But the thing that scared me most was when my enemy came close
    And I saw that his face looked just like mine."

    interlude
    Oh! Lord! Just like mine!

11. "And I couldn't help but think, through the thunder rolling and stink
    That I was just a puppet in a play.
    And through this roar and smoke this string is finally broke,
    And a cannon ball blew my eyes away."

12. As he turned away to walk his Ma was still in shock
    At seein' the metal brace that helped him stand.
    But as he turned to go, he called his mother close
    And he dropped his medals down into her hand.

It Ain't Me, Babe

Words and Music by Bob Dylan

72

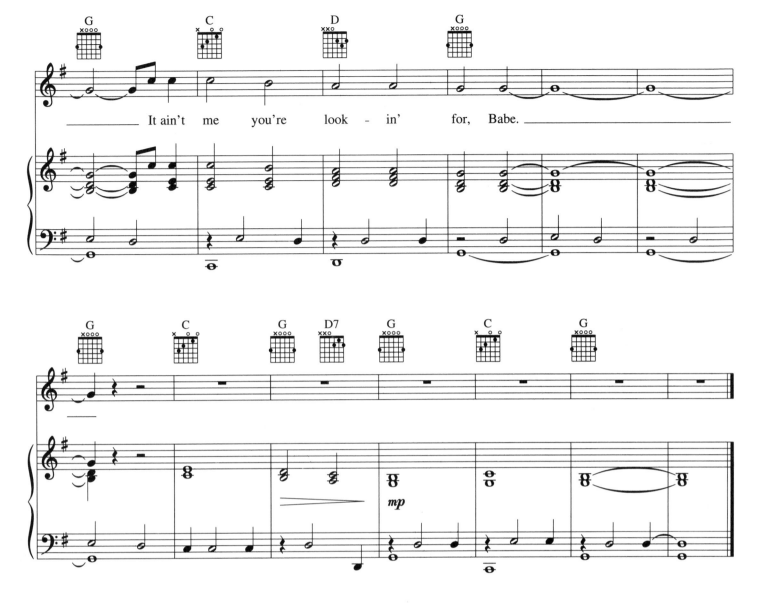

It ain't me you're look - in' for, Babe.

Additional lyrics

2. Go lightly from the ledge Babe,
   Go lightly on the ground,
   I'm not the one you want, Babe,
   I will only let you down.
   You say you're looking for someone
   Who will promise never to part,
   Someone to close his eyes for you
   Someone to close his heart.
   Someone who will die for you an' more
   But it ain't me, Babe,
   No, no, no it ain't me, Babe.
   It ain't me you're looking for, Babe.

3. Go melt back into the night Babe,
   Everything inside is made of stone,
   There's nothing in here moving
   An' anyway I'm not alone.
   You say you're looking for someone
   Who'll pick you up each time you fall,
   To gather flowers constantly
   An' to come each time you call.
   A lover for your life an' nothing more
   But it ain't me, Babe,
   No, no, no it ain't me, Babe.
   It ain't me you're looking for, Babe.

Just Like Tom Thumb's Blues

Words and Music by Bob Dylan

down on Rue Morgue Av-e-nue. _____ They got some hun-gry wom-en there And they real-ly make a mess out-ta you. _____

Repeat 5 times

2. Now if you see Saint Annie
   Please tell her thanks a lot
   I cannot move
   My fingers are all in a knot
   I don't have the strength
   To get up and take another shot
   And my best friend my doctor
   Won't even say what it is I've got

3. Sweet Melinda
   The peasants call her the goddess of gloom
   She speaks good English
   And she invites you up into her room
   And you're so kind
   And careful not to go to her too soon
   And she takes your voice
   And leaves you howling at the moon

4. Up on Housing Project Hill
   It's either fortune or fame
   You must pick up one or the other
   Though neither of them are to be what they claim
   If you're lookin' to get silly
   You better go back to from where you came
   Because the cops don't need you
   And man they expect the same

5. Now all the authorities
   They just stand around and boast
   How they blackmailed the sergeant at arms
   Into leaving his post
   And picking up Angel who
   Just arrived here from the coast
   Who looked so fine at first
   But left looking just like a ghost

6. I started out on burgundy
   But soon hit the harder stuff
   Everybody said they'd stand behind me
   When the game got rough
   But the joke was on me
   There was nobody even there to call my bluff
   I'm going back to New York City
   I do believe I've had enough

LAY DOWN YOUR WEARY TUNE

Words and Music by Bob Dylan

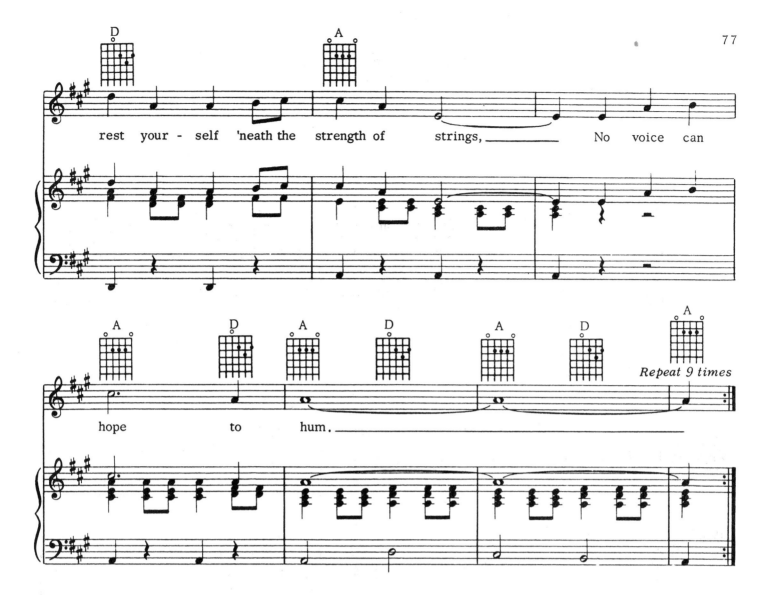

rest your-self 'neath the strength of strings, _____ No voice can hope to hum. _____

Repeat 9 times

2. Struck by the sounds before the sun,
   I knew the night had gone,
   The morning breeze like a bugle blew
   Against the drums of dawn.

3. Lay down your weary tune, lay down,
   Lay down the song you strum
   And rest yourself 'neath the strength of strings,
   No voice can hope to hum.

4. The ocean wild like an organ played
   The seaweed's wove its strands,
   The crashin' waves like cymbals clashed
   Against the rocks and sands.

5. Lay down your weary tune, lay down,
   Lay down the song you strum
   And rest yourself 'neath the strength of strings,
   No voice can hope to hum.

6. I stood unwound beneath the skies
   And clouds unbound by laws,
   The cryin' rain like a trumpet sang
   And asked for no applause.

7. Lay down your weary tune, lay down,
   Lay down the song you strum
   And rest yourself 'neath the strength of strings,
   No voice can hope to hum.

8. The last of leaves fell from the trees
   And clung to a new love's breast,
   The branches bare like a banjo
   To the winds that listen the best.

9. I gazed down in the river's mirror
   And watched its winding strum
   The water smooth ran like a hymn
   And like a harp did hum.

10. Lay down your weary tune, lay down,
    Lay down the song you strum
    And rest yourself 'neath the strength of strings,
    No voice can hope to hum.

Leopard-Skin Pill-Box Hat

WORDS AND MUSIC BY BOB DYLAN

1. Well, I

see you got your___ brand new leop-ard-skin pill - box___ hat___

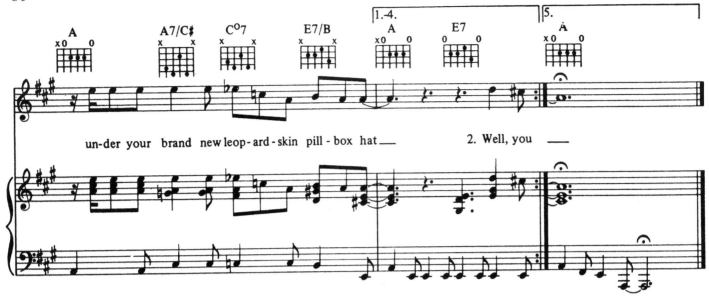

un-der your brand new leop-ard-skin pill-box hat____   2. Well, you ____

Additional Lyrics

2. Well, you look so pretty in it
   Honey, can I jump on it sometime?
   Yes, I just wanna see
   If it's really that expensive kind
   You know it balances on your head
   Just like a mattress balances
   On a bottle of wine
   Your brand new leopard-skin pill-box hat

3. Well, if you wanna see the sun rise
   Honey, I know where
   We'll go out and see it sometime
   We'll both just sit there and stare
   Me with my belt
   Wrapped around my head
   And you just sittin' there
   In your brand new leopard-skin pill-box hat

4. Well, I asked the doctor if I could see you
   It's bad for your health, he said
   Yes, I disobeyed his orders
   I came to see you
   But I found him there instead
   You know, I don't mind him cheatin' on me
   But I sure wish he'd take that off his head
   Your brand new leopard-skin pill-box hat

5. Well, I see you got a new boyfriend
   You know, I never seen him before
   Well, I saw him
   Makin' love to you
   You forgot to close the garage door
   You might think he loves you for your money
   But I know what he really loves you for
   It's your brand new leopard-skin pill-box hat

Maggie's Farm

Words and Music by Bob Dylan

Medium bright

1. I ain't gon - na work on MAG - GIE'S FARM no more ___

No, I ain't gon - na work on MAG - GIE'S

makes me scrub the floor _____ I ain't gon - na work on MAG- GIE'S

FARM no more. _____

Repeat 4 times

2. I ain't gonna work for Maggie's brother no more
No, I ain't gonna work for Maggie's brother no more
Well he hands you a nickel
He hands you a dime
He asks with a grin
If you're havin' a good time
Then he fines you every time you slam the door
I ain't gonna work for Maggie's brother no more.

3. I ain't gonna work for Maggie's pa no more
No, I ain't gonna work for Maggie's pa no more
Well he puts his cigar
Out in your face just for kicks
His bedroom window
It is made out of bricks
The National Guard stands around his door
Ah, I ain't gonna work for Maggie's pa no more.

4. I ain't gonna work for Maggie's ma no more
No, I ain't gonna work for Maggie's ma no more
Well she talks to all the servants
About man and God and law
Everybody says she's the brains behind pa
She's sixty-eight, but she says she's twenty-four
I ain't gonna work for Maggie's ma no more.

5. I ain't gonna work on Maggie's farm no more
I ain't gonna work on Maggie's farm no more
Well, I try my best
To be just like I am
But everybody wants you
To be just like them
They sing while you slave
And I just get bored
I ain't gonna work on Maggie's farm no more.

Like A Rolling Stone

WORDS AND MUSIC BY BOB DYLAN

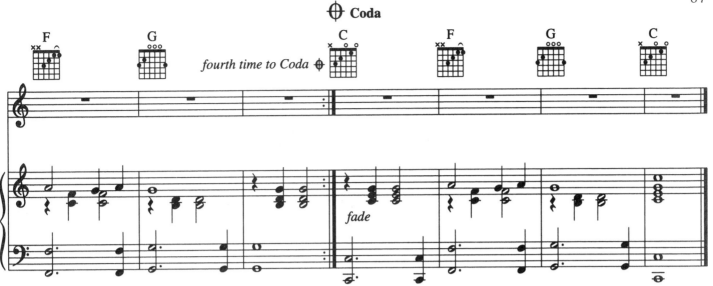

Additional lyrics

2. You've gone to the finest school all right Miss Lonely
   But you know you only used to get juiced in it
   And nobody's every taught you how to live on the street
   And now find out you're gonna have to get used to it
   You said you'd never compromise
   With the mystery tramp, but now you realize
   He's not selling any alibis
   As you stare into the vacuum of his eyes
   And ask him do you want to make a deal?
   Chorus

3. You never turned around to see the frowns on the jugglers and the clowns
   When they all come down and did tricks for you
   You never understood that it ain't no good
   You shouldn't let other people get your kicks for you
   You used to ride on the chrome horse with your diplomat
   Who carried on his shoulder a Siamese cat
   Ain't it hard when you discovered that
   He really wasn't where it's at
   After he took from you everything he could steal.
   Chorus

4. Princess on the steeple and all the pretty people
   They're drinkin', thinkin' that they got it made
   Exchanging all kinds of precious gifts and things
   But you'd better lift your diamond ring, you'd better pawn it babe
   You used to be so amused
   At Napoleon in rags and the language that he used
   Go to him now, he calls you, you can't refuse
   When you got nothing, you got nothing to lose
   You're invisible now, you got no secrets to conceal.
   Chorus

Love Minus Zero/No Limit

Words and Music by Bob Dylan

Additional lyrics

2. In the dime stores and bus stations,
   People talk of situations,
   Read books, repeat quotations,
   Draw conclusions on the wall.
   Some speak of the future,
   My love, she speaks softly,
   She know there's no success like failure
   and that failure's no success at all.

3. The cloak and dagger dangles,
   Madams light the candles.
   In ceremonies of the horsemen,
   Even the pawn must hold a grudge.
   Statues made of match sticks,
   Crumble into one another,
   My love winks, she does not bother,
   She knows too much to argue or to judge.

4. The bridge at midnight trembles,
   The country doctor rambles,
   Bankers' nieces seek perfection,
   Expecting all the gifts that wise men bring.
   The wind howls like a hammer,
   The night blows cold an' rainy,
   My love she's like some raven
   At my window with a broken wing.

Masters Of War

Words and Music by Bob Dylan

walls   You that hide   be-hind desks   I just

want you to know I can see through your masks

D.S. 𝄋

2. You that never done nothin'
   But build to destroy
   You play with my world
   Like it's your little toy
   You put a gun in my hand
   And you hide from my eyes
   And you turn and run farther
   When the fast bullets fly

3. Like Judas of old
   You lie and deceive
   A world war can be won
   You want me to believe
   But I see through your eyes
   And I see through your brain
   Like I see through the water
   That runs down my drain

4. You fasten the triggers
   For the others to fire
   Then you set back and watch
   When the death count gets higher
   You hide in your mansion
   As young people's blood
   Flows out of their bodies
   And is buried in the mud

5. You've thrown the worst fear
   That can ever be hurled
   Fear to bring children
   Into the world
   For threatenin' my baby
   Unborn and unnamed
   You ain't worth the blood
   That runs in your veins

6. How much do I know
   To talk out of turn
   You might say that I'm young
   You might say I'm unlearned
   But there's one thing I know
   Though I'm younger than you
   Even Jesus would never
   Forgive what you do

7. Let me ask you one questions
   Is your money that good
   Will it buy you forgiveness
   Do you think that it could
   I think you will find
   When your death takes its toll
   All the money you made
   Will never buy back your soul

8. And I hope that you die
   And your death'll come soon
   I will follow your casket
   On a pale afternoon
   And I'll watch while you're lowered
   Down to your death bed
   And I'll stand o'er your grave
   Till I'm sure that you're dead.

MOST LIKELY YOU GO YOUR WAY (AND I'LL GO MINE)

WORDS AND MUSIC BY BOB DYLAN

But he's bad - ly built And he walks on stilts, Watch out he don't fall on you. mine.

Repeat and fade

Repeat and fade

Mr. Tambourine Man

Words and Music by Bob Dylan

brand - ed on my feet. I have no one to meet and the

Repeat three times

an - cient emp - ty street's too dead for dream in'. _____

Refrain:

Verse 2. Take me on a trip upon your magic swirlin' ship
My senses have been stripped, my hands can't feel to grip
My toes too numb to step, wait only for my boot heels
To be wanderin'
I'm ready to go anywhere, I'm ready for to fade
Into my own parade, cast your dancin' spell my way
I promise to go under it.

Refrain:

Verse 3. Though you might hear laughin' spinnin' swingin' madly across the sun
It's not aimed at anyone, it's just escapin' on the run
And but for the sky there are no fences facin'
And if you hear vague traces of skippin' reels of rhyme
To your tambourine in time, it's just a ragged clown behind
I wouldn't pay it any mind, it's just a shadow you're
Seein' that he's chasin'.

Refrain:

Verse 4. Then take me disappearin' through the smoke rings of my mind
Down the foggy ruins of time, far past the frozen leaves
The haunted, frightened trees out to the windy beach
Far from the twisted reach of crazy sorrow
Yes, to dance beneath the diamond sky with one hand wavin' free
Silhouetted by the sea, circled by the circus sands
With all memory and fate driven deep beneath the waves
Let me forget about today until tomorrow.

Refrain:

My Back Pages

Words and Music by Bob Dylan

1. Crim - son flames tied through my ears, Rol - lin'

2.-6. *See additional lyrics*

high and might - y traps, _____ Pounced with

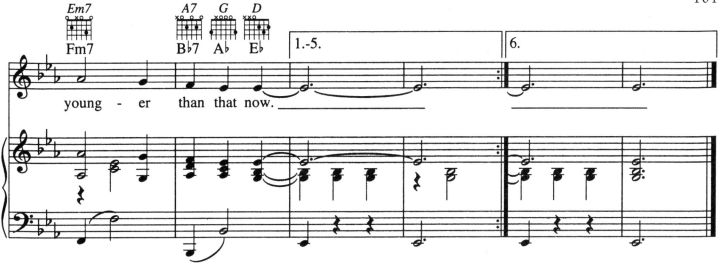

young - er than that now._____

2. Half-wracked prejudice leaped forth,
   "Rip down all here," I screamed,
   Lies that life is black and white
   Spoke from my skull I dreamed.
   Romantic facts of musketeers,
   Foundationed deep, somehow,
   Ah, but I was so much older then,
   I'm younger than that now.

4. A self-ordained professor's tongue,
   Too serious to fool,
   Spouted out that liberty.
   Is just equality in school.
   "Equality," I spoke the word
   As if a wedding vow,
   Ah, but I was so much older then,
   I'm younger than that now.

3. Girl's faces formed the forward path
   From phony jealousy,
   To memorizing politics
   Of ancient history.
   Flung down by corpse evangelist
   Unthought of, though, somehow,
   Ah, but I was so much older then,
   I'm younger than that now.

5. In a soldier's stance I aimed my hand
   At the mongrel dogs who teach,
   Fearing not that I'd become my enemy
   In the instant that I preach.
   My pathway led by confusion boats,
   Mutiny from stern to bow,
   Ah, but I was so much older then,
   I'm younger than that now.

6. Yes, my guards stood hard when abstract threats
   Too noble to neglect
   Deceived me into thinking
   I had something to protect.
   Good and bad, I define these terms
   Quite clear, no doubt, somehow,
   Ah, but I was so much older then,
   I'm younger than that, now.

New Morning

Words and Music by Bob Dylan

Moderately fast

Can't you hear that___ roost-er crow-in'?___
Can't you hear that___ mo-tor turn-in'?___

Rab-bit run-nin' down a-cross the road
Au-to-mo-bile com-in' in-to style,

ONE MORE CUP OF COFFEE (VALLEY BELOW)

WORDS AND MUSIC BY BOB DYLAN

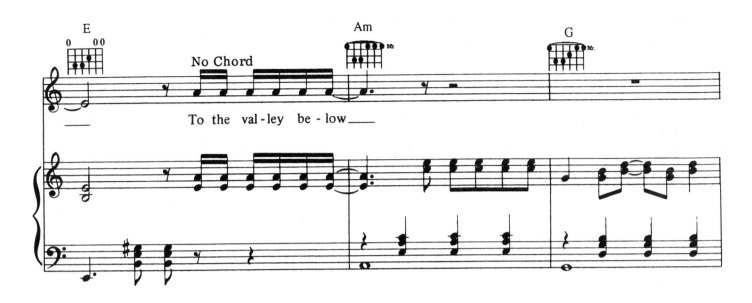

To the val-ley be-low____

2. Your
3. Your

2.   Your daddy he's an outlaw
And a wanderer by trade
He'll teach you how to pick and choose
And how to throw the blade
He oversees his kingdom
So no stranger does intrude
His voice it trembles as he calls out for
Another plate of food

One more cup of coffee for the road
One more cup of coffee 'fore I go
To the valley below

3.   Your sister sees the future
Like your mama and yourself
You've never learned to read or write
There's no books upon your shelf
And your pleasure knows no limits
Your voice is like a meadow lark
But your heart is like an ocean
Mysterious and dark

One more cup of coffee for the road
One more cup of coffee 'fore I go
To the valley below

Political World

Words and Music by Bob Dylan

Brightly, with a driving beat (in4)

1. We live in a po-lit-i-cal world,— Love don't have an-y place.— We're liv-ing in times where men— com-mit crimes, And crime—

Life is in mir-rors, death dis-ap-pears Up the steps in-to the near-est bank._

Gm

1. 2.

5. We

Gomit3rd
x 0 0

live in a po-lit-i-cal world_ Where cour-age is a thing of the past,_

Hous-es are haunt-ed, chil-dren are un-want-ed, The next day could be your last._ 6. We

114

Lit - tle by lit - tle you turn in the mid - dle, But you're nev - er sure why you're here.___ 8. We

live in a po - lit - i - cal world,___ Un - der the mi - cro - scope,___ You can

trav - el an - y - where and hang___ your - self there, You al - ways got more than e - nough rope.

Gm

9. We

live in a po-lit-i-cal world,_ Turn-ing and a-thrash-ing a-bout._ As

soon as you're a-wake, you're trained_ to take_ What looks like the eas-y way out._

10. We

live in a po-lit-i-cal world_ Where peace is not wel-come at all,_ It's turned a-

way from the door_ to wan-der some more_ Or put up a-gainst the wall. _ 11. We

live in a po-lit-i-cal world,_ Ev-ery-thing is hers_ or his,_

Climb in-to the frame and shout_ God's name, But you're nev-er sure what it is.__

Gm

Repeat and fade

Positively Fourth Street

Words and Music by Bob Dylan

Medium tempo

twelfth time to Coda

repeat eleven times

You got a lot-ta nerve ___ To say you are my friend

When I was down You just stood there grin-ning ___

Coda

2. You got a lotta nerve
   To say you gotta helping hand to lend
   You just want to be on
   The side that's winning

3. You say I let you down
   You know it's not like that
   If you're so hurt
   Why then don't you show it

4. You say you lost your faith
   But that's not where it's at
   You had no faith to lose
   And you know it

5. I know the reason
   That you talk behind my back
   I used to be among the crowd
   You're in with

6. Do you take me for such a fool
   To think I'd make contact
   With the one who tries to hide
   When he don't know to begin with

7. You see me on the street
   You always act surprised
   You say "how are you?", "good luck"
   But you don't mean it

8. When you know as well as me
   You'd rather see me paralyzed
   Why don't you just come out once
   And scream it

9. No I do not feel that good
   When I see the heart breaks you embrace
   If I was a master thief
   Perhaps I'd rob them

10. And now I know you're dissatisfied
    With your position and your place
    Don't you understand
    It's not my problem

11. I wish that for just one time
    You could stand inside my shoes
    And just for that one moment
    I could be you

12. Yes I wish that for just one time
    You could stand inside my shoes
    You'd know what a drag it is
    To see you

RING THEM BELLS

Words and Music by Bob Dylan

121

122

126

SEVEN DAYS

WORDS AND MUSIC BY BOB DYLAN

Moderately (in 2)

Sev - en days,

131

She Belongs To Me

Words and Music by Bob Dylan

art - ist   She don't   look   back   She can take the

dark   out of the night-time And ___ paint   the day - time   black.

Repeat 4 times

2. You will start out standing
   Proud to steal her anything she sees
   You will start out standing
   Proud to steal her anything she sees
   But you will wind up peeking through her keyhole
   Down upon your knees.

3. She never stumbles
   She's got no place to fall
   She never stumbles
   She's got no place to fall
   She's nobody's child
   The law can't touch her at all.

4. She wears an Egyptian ring
   That sparkles before she speaks
   She wears an Egyptian ring
   That sparkles before she speaks
   She is a hypnotist collector
   You are a walking antique.

5. Bow down to her on Sunday
   Salute her when her birthday comes
   Bow down to her on Sunday
   Salute her when her birthday comes
   For Halloween give her a trumpet
   And for Christmas, buy her a drum.

SHOOTING STAR

WORDS AND MUSIC BY BOB DYLAN

140

shoot - ing star to - night__   slip a - way.__

Tonight I'll Be Staying Here With You

Words and Music by Bob Dylan

Subterranean Homesick Blues

Words and Music by Bob Dylan

Moderate blues rock

1. John - ny's in the base - ment mix - ing up the med - i - cine; I'm on the pave - ment

think - ing a - bout the gov - ern - ment. The man in the trench coat,

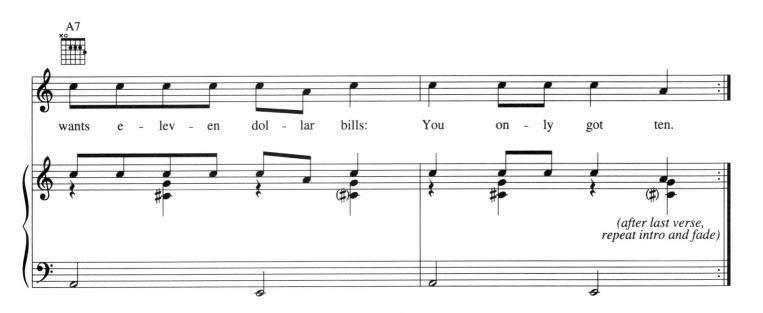

A7

wants e – lev – en dol – lar bills: You on – ly got ten.

*(after last verse,
repeat intro and fade)*

2. Maggie comes fleet foot
   Face full of black soot
   Talkin' at the heat put
   Plants in the bed but
   The phone's tapped any-way
   Maggie says that many say
   They must bust in early May
   Orders from the D.A.
   Look out kid
   Don't matter what you did
   Walk on your tip toes
   Don't try "No Doz"
   Better stay away from those
   That carry around a fire hose
   Keep a clean nose
   Watch the plain clothes
   You don't need a weather man
   To know which way the wind blows.

3. Get sick, get well
   Hang around a ink well
   Ring bell, hard to tell
   If anything is goin' to sell
   Try hard, get barred
   Get back, write braille
   Get jailed, jump bail
   Join the army, if you fail
   Look out kid, you're gonna get hit
   But users, cheaters
   Six time losers
   Hang around the theatres
   Girl by the whirlpool
   Lookin' for a new fool
   Don't follow leaders
   Watch the parkin' meters

4. Ah get born, keep warm
   Short pants, romance, learn to dance
   Get dressed, get blessed
   Try to be a success
   Please her, please him, buy gifts
   Don't steal, don't lift
   Twenty years of schoolin'
   And they put you on the day shift
   Look out kid they keep it all hid
   Better jump down a manhole
   Light yourself a candle, don't wear sandals
   Try to avoid the scandals
   Don't wanna be a bum
   You better chew gum
   The pump don't work
   'Cause the vandals took the handles.

The Times They Are A-Changin'

Words and Music by Bob Dylan

Moderately

1. Come gath-er 'round peo-ple where-ev-er you roam _____ And ad-
2.-5. *See additional lyrics*

mit that the wa-ters a-round you have grown And ac-cept it that

soon you'll be drenched to the bone. _____ If your time to you is worth

Additional lyrics

2. Come writers and critics who prophecize with your pen
And keep your eyes wide the chance won't come again
And don't speak too soon for the wheel's still in spin
And there's no tellin' who that it's namin'.
For the loser now will be later to win
For the times they are a-changin'.

3. Come senators, congressmen please heed the call
Don't stand in the doorway don't block the hall
For he that gets hurt will be he who has stalled
There's a battle outside and it's ragin'.
It'll soon shake your windows and rattle your walls
For the times they are a-changin'.

4. Come mothers and fathers throughout the land
And don't criticize what you can't understand
Your sons and your daughters are beyond your command
Your old road is rapidly agin'.
Please get out of the new one if you can't lend your hand
For the times they are a-changin'.

5. The line it is drawn the curse it is cast
The slow one now will later be fast
As the present now will later be past
The order is rapidly fadin'.
And the first one now will later be last
For the times they are a-changin'.

Up To Me

Words and Music by Bob Dylan

156

2. If I'd of thought about it I never would've done it
   I guess I would-a let it slide
   If I'd-a lived my life by what others were thinkin'
   The heart inside me would-a died
   I was just too stubborn to ever be governed
   By enforced insanity
   Someone had to reach for the risin' star
   I guess it was up to me

3. Oh, the Union Central is pullin' out
   And the orchids are in bloom
   I've only got me one good shirt left
   And it smells of stale perfume
   In fourteen months I've only smiled once
   And I didn't do it consciously
   Somebody's got to find your trail
   I guess it must be up to me

4. It was like a revelation
   When you betrayed me with your touch
   I'd just about convinced myself
   That nothin' had changed that much
   The old Rounder in the iron mask
   Slipped me the master key
   Somebody had to unlock your heart
   He said it was up to me

5. Well, I watched you slowly disappear
   Down into the officers' club
   I would've followed you in the door
   But I didn't have a ticket stub
   So I waited all night 'til the break of day
   Hopin' one of us could get free
   When the dawn came over the river bridge
   I knew it was up to me

6. Oh, the only decent thing I did
   When I worked as a postal clerk
   Was to haul your picture down off the wall
   Near the cage where I used to work
   Was I a fool or not to try
   To protect your identity
   You looked a little burned out, my friend
   I thought it might be up to me

7. Well, I met somebody face to face
   And I had to remove my hat
   She's everything I need and love
   But I can't be swayed by that
   It frightens me, the awful truth
   Of how sweet life can be
   But she ain't a-gonna make a move
   I guess it must be up to me

8. We heard the Sermon on the Mount
   And I knew it was too complex
   It didn't amount to anything more
   Than what the broken glass reflects
   When you bite off more than you can chew
   You pay the penalty
   Somebody's got to tell the tale
   I guess it must be up to me

9. Well, Dupree came in pimpin' tonight
   To the Thunderbird Cafe
   Crystal wanted to talk to him
   I had to look the other way
   Well, I just can't rest without you, love
   I need your company
   But you ain't a-gonna cross the line
   I guess it must be up to me

10. There's a note left in the bottle
    You can give it to Estelle
    She's the one you been wondrin' about
    But there's really nothin' much to tell
    We both heard voices for awhile
    Now the rest is history
    Somebody's got to cry some tears
    I guess it must be up to me

11. So go on boys and play your hands
    Life is a pantomime
    The ringleaders from the county seat
    Say you don't have all that much time
    And the girl with me behind the shades
    She ain't my property
    One of us has got to hit the road
    I guess it must be up to me

12. And if we never meet again
    Baby remember me
    How my lone guitar played sweet for you
    That old-time melody
    And the harmonica around my neck
    I blew it for you, free
    No one else could play that tune
    You know it was up to me

This Wheel's On Fire

WORDS BY BOB DYLAN, MUSIC BY RICK DANKO

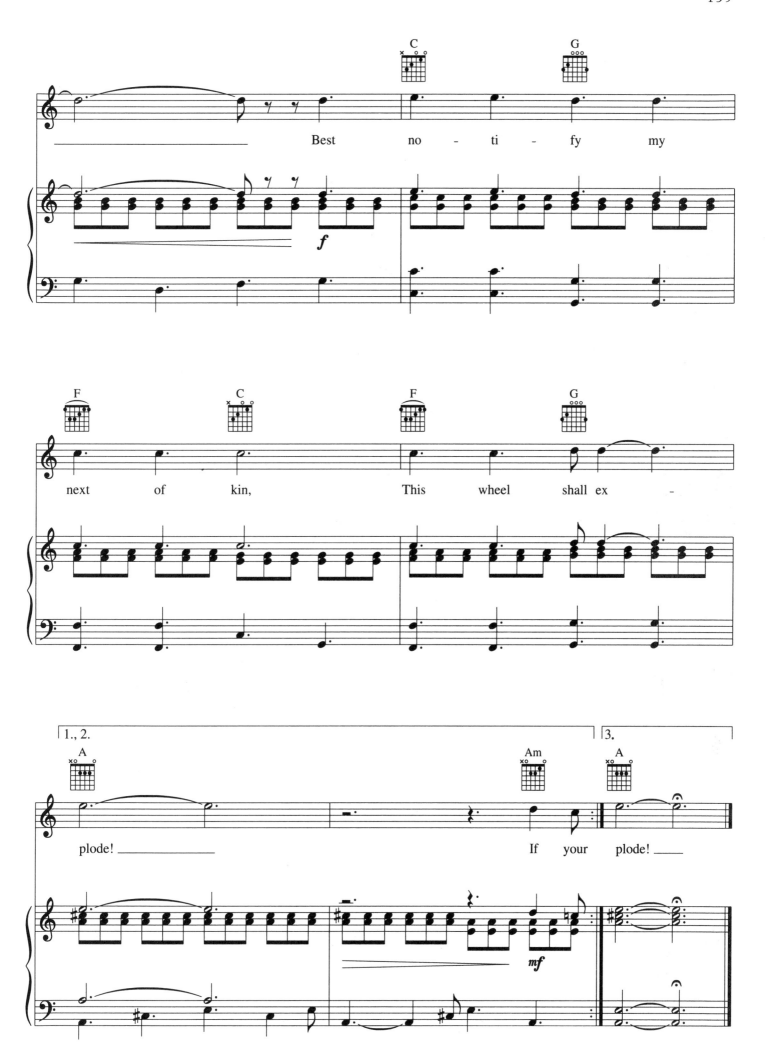

Tombstone Blues

Words and Music by Bob Dylan

Additional lyrics

2. The hysterical bride in the penny arcade
   Screaming she moans, "I've just been made"
   Then sends out for the doctor who pulls down the shade
   Says, "My advice is to not let the boys in"

   Now the medicine man comes and he shuffles inside
   He walks with a swagger and he says to the bride,
   "Stop all this weeping, swallow your pride
   You will not die, it's not poison"
   Chorus

3. Well, John the Baptist after torturing a thief
   Looks up at his hero the Commander-in-Chief
   Saying, "Tell me great hero, but please make it brief
   Is there a hole for me to get sick in?"

   The Commander-in-Chief answers him while chasing a fly
   Saying, "Death to all those who would whimper and cry"
   And dropping a barbell he points to the sky
   Saying, "The sun's not yellow it's chicken"
   Chorus

4. The king of the Philistines his soldiers to save
   Put jawbones on their tombstones and flatters their graves
   Puts the pied pipers in prison and fattens the slaves
   Then sends them out to the jungle

   Gypsy Davey with a blow torch he burns out their camps
   With his faithful slave Pedro behind him he tramps
   With a fantastic collection of stamps
   To win friends and influence his uncle
   Chorus

5. The geometry of innocence flesh on the bone
   Causes Galileo's math book to get thrown
   At Delilah who sits worthlessly alone
   But the tears on her cheeks are from laughter

   Now I wish I could give Brother Bill his great thrill
   I would set him in chains at the top of the hill
   Then send out for some pillars and Cecil B. DeMille
   He could die happily ever after
   Chorus

6. Where Ma Rainey and Beethoven once unwrapped their bed roll
   Tuba players now rehearse around the flagpole
   And the National Bank at a profit sells road maps for the soul
   To the old folks home and the college

   Now I wish I could write you a melody so plain
   That could hold you dear lady from going insane
   That could ease you and cool you and cease the pain
   Of your useless and pointless knowledge
   Chorus

Too Much Of Nothing

WORDS AND MUSIC BY BOB DYLAN

Wiggle Wiggle

Words and Music by Bob Dylan

roll - ing hoop.__   Wig - gle, wig - gle, wig - gle like a ton of lead,__

Wig - gle, you can raise__ the dead.   snake.
(Wig - gle like a big fat)

Additional Lyrics

Bridge:

Wiggle 'til you're high, wiggle 'til you're higher,
Wiggle 'til you vomit fire,
Wiggle 'til it whispers, wiggle 'til it hums,
Wiggle 'til it answers, wiggle 'til it comes.

Wiggle, wiggle, wiggle like satin and silk,
Wiggle, wiggle, wiggle like a pail of milk.
Wiggle, wiggle, wiggle, rattle and shake,
Wiggle like a big fat snake.

Watching The River Flow

Words and Music by Bob Dylan

night ca - fé.
hand.

Walk-in' to and fro ___ be-neath the moon
If I had wings ___ and I could fly,

Out to where the

trucks are _____ roll - 'in slow,
I know where I would go.

To
But

sit down on ___ this bank of sand _____ And watch the
right now ___ I'll just sit here so con - tent - ed - ly And watch the

When The Night Comes Falling From The Sky

Words and Music by Bob Dylan

Verse 1. Look out a-cross the fields,_____ see me re-turn-ing.

Smoke is in___ your eye,___ you draw a smile;___

when the night_ comes fall - ing from the sky.____

Verse 2. I can see_

Repeat and fade

180

```
        ‖ Bbm              |Gb/Bb          |Bbm    |Gb/Bb |
Verse 2.  I can see through your walls and I know you're hurting,
        Bbm              |Gb            |
        sorrow covers you up like a cape.              Only
        Gb7              |              |Bbm   |
        yesterday I know that you've been flirting      with dis-
        Db6              |         F7+5 |F7   ‖
        aster that you managed to escape.          I
        Bbm              |              |      |
        can't provide for you no easy answers.
                                        |Gb    |      |
        Who are you that I should have to lie?      You'll know
        Gb7              |Ab           |Bbm
        all about it, love      it'll fit you like a glove
        Gb   |Bbm              |Gb    |Bbm         |
                  when the night comes falling,    when the night comes
        Gb   |Bbm              |Gb    |Bbm     |
        falling,  when the night comes falling from the sky.
        Gb         |Bbm       |Gb    ‖
```

```
        ‖ Bbm              |Gb/Bb          |Bbm |Gb/Bb  |
Verse 3.  I can hear your trembling heart beat like a river, you must have
        Bbm              |Gb            |
        been protecting someone last time I called.      I've never
        Gb7              |              |Bbm   |      |
        asked you for nothing you couldn't deliver,      I've never
        Db7              |         F7+5 |F7   ‖
        asked you to set yourself up for a fall.          I saw
        Bbm                             |      |      |
        thousands who could have overcome the darkness,      for the
                                        |Gb    |      |
        love of a lousy buck, I've watched them die,    Stick a-
        Gb7              |              |Ab   |Bbm   |
        round baby, we're not through, don't look for me, I'll see you
        Gb   |Bbm              |Gb    |Bbm         |
                  when the night comes falling,    when the night comes
        Gb   |Bbm              |Gb    |Bbm     |
        falling,  when the night comes falling from the sky.
        Gb         |Bbm       |Gb    ‖
```

‖ **Bbm**　　　|**Gb/Bb**　　|**Bbm**　|**Gb/Bb**　　　|

Verse 4.　In your teardrops I can see my own reflection,　it was on the

Bbm　　　　　|　　　　　　|**Gb**　　　|　　　　　|

northern border of Texas where I crossed the line.　　　I don't

Gb7　　　|　　　　|**Bbm**　|　　　　|

want to be a fool starving for affection,　　I don't

Db6　　　|　　　　**F7+5**|**F7**　　　‖

want to drown in someone else's wine.　　　For all e -

Bbm　|　　|　　|　　|

ternity I think I will remember　　　that

　　|　　|**Gb**　|　　|

icy wind that's howling in your eye.　　You will

Gb7　|　|**Ab**　|**Bbm**　|

seek me and you'll find me in the wasteland of your mind

Gb　|**Bbm**　|**Gb**　|**Bbm**　|

　　when the night comes falling,　when the night comes

Gb　|**Bbm**　|**Gb**　|**Bbm**　|

falling,　when the night comes falling from the sky.

Gb　　|**Bbm**　|**Gb**　‖

‖ **Bbm**　　|**Gb/Bb**　|**Bbm**　|**Gb/Bb**　|

Verse 5.　Well, I sent you my feelings in a letter　　but

Bbm　　|　　|**Gb**　|　　|

you were gambling　for support.

Gb7　|　|**Bbm**　|　|

This time tomorrow I'll know you better

Db6　|　**F7+5**|**F7**　‖

when my memory is not so short.

Bbm　|　|　|　|

This time I'm asking for freedom,

　|　|**Gb**　|　|

freedom from a world which you deny.　　And you'll

Gb7　|**Ab**　|**Bbm**　|　|

give it to my now, I'll take it any-how,

Gb　|**Bbm**　|**Gb**　|**Bbm**　|

　　when the night comes falling,　when the night comes

Gb　|**Bbm**　|**Gb**　|**Bbm**　|

falling,　when the night comes falling from the sky.

Gb　|**Bbm**　|**Gb**　‖

Instrumental and fade

WHEN THE SHIP COMES IN

WORDS AND MUSIC BY BOB DYLAN

Medium bright

1. Oh the time will come up when the winds will stop And the breeze will cease to be breath-in' ____ Like the still-ness in the wind 'Fore the hur-ri-cane be-gins The ho-ur when the ship comes in. Oh the seas will split And the ship will hit And the

shore-line   sands will be shak-ing _____ Then the tide   will sound And the wind   will pound And the

morn-ing   will   be   break   -   ing. _____

D.S.
three times 𝄉

2. Oh the fishes will laugh
    As they swim out of the path
    And the seagulls they'll be smiling
    And the rocks on the sand
    Will proudly stand
    The hour that the ship comes in.

    And the words they use
    For to get the ship confused
    Will not be understood as they're spoken
    For the chains of the sea
    Will have busted in the night
    And will be buried at the bottom of the ocean.

3. A song will lift
    As the mainsail shifts
    And the boat drifts on to the shore line
    And the sun will respect
    Every face on the deck
    The hour when the ship comes in.

    Then the sands will roll
    Out a carpet of gold
    For your weary toes to be a touchin'
    And the ship's wise men
    Will remind you once again
    That the whole wide world is watchin'.

4. Oh the foes will rise
    With the sleep still in their eyes
    And they'll jerk from their beds and think they're dreamin'
    But they'll pinch themselves and squeal
    And know that it's for real
    The hour when the ship comes in.

    Then they'll raise their hands
    Sayin' we'll meet all your demands
    But we'll shout from the bow your days are numbered
    And like Pharaoh's triumph
    They'll be drowned in the tide
    And like Goliath they'll be conquered.

Unbelievable

Words and Music by Bob Dylan

It's un-be-liev-a-ble, it's strange but true.__

It's in-con-ceiv-a-ble it could hap-pen to you.__

they say____ it's the land____ of mon - ey.

Who - ev - er thought ____ they could ev - er make____ that stick.____

C7

F7(#9)

It's un - be - liev - a - ble you

can get this rich this quick.

liev - a - ble   it   would   go   down this   way. ___

Bridge:

Once there was a man who had no eyes,
Every lady in the land told him lies,
He stood beneath the silver skies
And his heart began to bleed.
Every brain is civilized,
Every nerve is analyzed,
Everything is criticized when you are in need.

It's unbelievable, it's fancy-free,
So interchangeable, so delightful to see.
Turn your back, wash your hands,
There's always someone who understands
It don't matter no more what you got to say
It's unbelievable it would go down this way.

You're A Big Girl Now

Words and Music by Bob Dylan

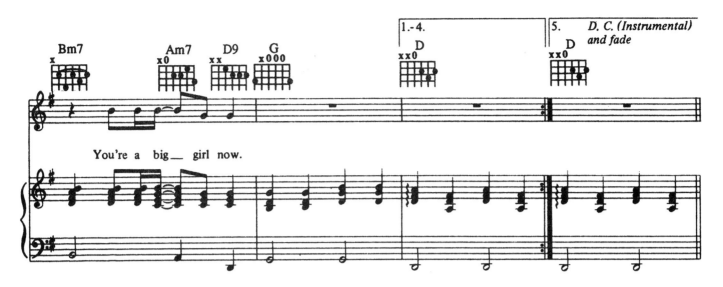

You're a big____ girl now.

2. Bird on the horizon
   Sittin' on a fence
   He's singin' his song for me
   At his own expense
   And I'm just like that bird
   Oh-oh
   Singin' just for you
   I hope that you can hear
   Hear me singin' through these tears

3. Time is a jet plane
   It moves too fast
   Oh, but what a shame
   If all we've shared can't last
   I can change, I swear
   Oh-oh
   See what you can do
   I can make it through
   You can make it too

4. Love is so simple
   To quote a phrase
   You've known it all the time
   I'm learnin' it these days
   Oh, I know where I can find you
   Oh-oh
   In somebody's room
   It's a price I have to pay
   You're a big girl all the way

5. A change in the weather
   Is known to be extreme
   But what's the sense of changing
   Horses in midstream
   I'm going out of my mind
   Oh-oh
   With a pain that stops and starts
   Like a corkscrew to my heart
   Ever since we've been apart

VISIONS OF JOHANNA
WORDS AND MUSIC BY BOB DYLAN

ise   holds a hand-ful of rain,   tempt-in' you_ to de -
hear   the night watch – man click his flash - light Ask him-self if it's him or them that's real - ly in-to
bring - ing her name up   He speaks of a fare-well kiss_ to
Li - sa must - a had the high - way blues   You can tell_ by the way she

fy it _____   Lights   flick - er from_ the op - po - site
sane_____   Lou - ise,   she's all right, she's just
me_____   He's   sure got_ a lot - ta
smiles_____   See   the prim - i - tive_ wall - flow - er

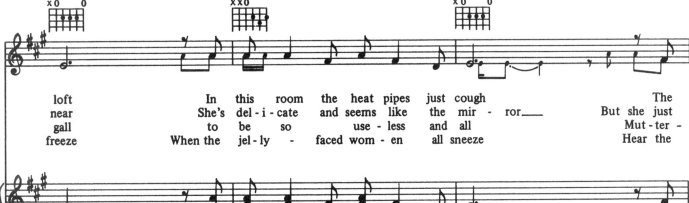

loft   In   this   room   the heat pipes just cough   The
near   She's del - i -cate and seems like the mir - ror_   But she just
gall   to   be   so   use - less and all   Mut - ter -
freeze   When the jel - ly - faced wom - en all sneeze   Hear the